Spotter's Guide to
MUSHROOMS
& other fungi

Richard Clarl
Tutor in Conservation, L

Illustrated by

with additional illus

Contents

The editor would like to thank Ray Cowell and Ted Ellis for their help.

Designed by
Sally Burrough

Series Editor
Bridget Gibbs

Edited by
Helen Gilks

First published in 1980 by
Usborne Publishing Limited,
20 Garrick Street, London WC2

Printed in Spain

How to use this book

This book will help you to identify many of the mushrooms, toadstools and other fungi that grow in Britain and Europe. Take it with you when you go out spotting.

Although most fungi appear in autumn, some interesting species (or kinds) can be found at other times of the year. Page 56 tells you where to look and what to take with you. When you find a fungus, first turn to pages 4 and 5. The information on these pages tells you which section of the book to turn to, and what to look for when identifying fungi.

Each picture shows the mature (fully grown) stage of a fungus and very often a young stage and a cross-section are also shown. Beside each picture is a description which tells you when and where it grows and gives its size. Next to each description is a blank circle. When you spot that fungus, make a tick in the circle.

Some fungi are quite difficult to identify and may not look exactly like their picture, so it is very important to read the description and notes around the picture.

Scientific names

The scientific name of each fungus is given under its English name. Some species have only a scientific name. The first word of the scientific name is the group that the fungus belongs to. The second word is the name of the species.

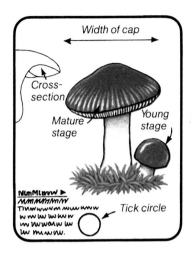

Measurements

Measurements given for mushrooms, toadstools and bracket fungi are for the width of the cap. For other fungi, without a cap, measurements are for the height or width of the whole fungus. As each kind of fungus varies in size, depending on the conditions that it grows in, a maximum and minimum size is given for the mature stage.

Scorecard

The scorecard at the end of the book gives you a score for each fungus you spot. A common fungus scores 5 points, and a rare one is worth 25 points. You can add up your score after a day out spotting.

Warning

A few fungi are deadly **poisonous**. Some edible and harmless fungi look very similar to those which are poisonous. So **never eat or taste** any fungus, unless an expert has helped you identify it.

Different types of fungi

Fungi are "plants" that cannot make their own food and so have to live off other plants or animals (see page 51). There are many thousands of different fungi, ranging in size and shape from tiny moulds to large bracket fungi. This book shows only some of the larger ones that belong to the groups illustrated below. To find out more about them, turn to the page listed beside each picture.

All the illustrations in this book show the fruit bodies of fungi. Each fruit body produces thousands of tiny dust-like spores from which new fungi can grow (see page 54). The main part of the fungus exists as a mass of tiny threads, known as "mycelium". Fungus mycelium lives all year round buried in the plant or animal matter that it feeds on. If you pick a mushroom or toadstool, you will see some of the mycelium attached to the base of the stem.

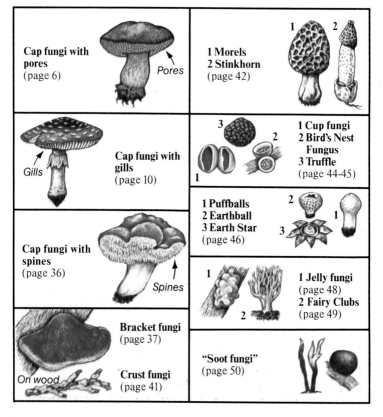

Cap fungi with pores
(page 6)
Pores

**1 Morels
2 Stinkhorn**
(page 42)

Gills

Cap fungi with gills
(page 10)

**1 Cup fungi
2 Bird's Nest Fungus
3 Truffle**
(page 44-45)

**1 Puffballs
2 Earthball
3 Earth Star**
(page 46)

Cap fungi with spines
(page 36)
Spines

1 Jelly fungi
(page 48)
2 Fairy Clubs
(page 49)

Bracket fungi
(page 37)

On wood

Crust fungi
(page 41)

"Soot fungi"
(page 50)

Identifying mushrooms & toadstools

In this book only the cap fungi with gills belonging to the *Agaricus* group (page 14) are called mushrooms. The word "toadstool" is used for all other cap fungi, whether they have gills, pores or spines. This page tells you what to note when identifying a mushroom or toadstool.

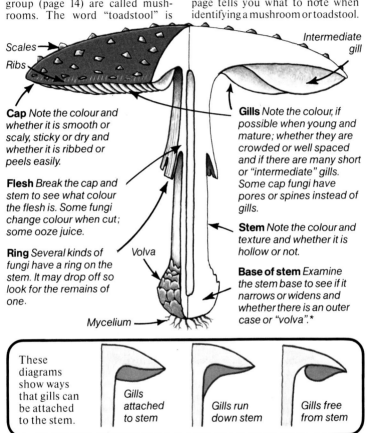

Scales

Ribs

Intermediate gill

Cap Note the colour and whether it is smooth or scaly, sticky or dry and whether it is ribbed or peels easily.

Flesh Break the cap and stem to see what colour the flesh is. Some fungi change colour when cut; some ooze juice.

Ring Several kinds of fungi have a ring on the stem. It may drop off so look for the remains of one.

Volva

Mycelium

Gills Note the colour, if possible when young and mature; whether they are crowded or well spaced and if there are many short or "intermediate" gills. Some cap fungi have pores or spines instead of gills.

Stem Note the colour and texture and whether it is hollow or not.

Base of stem Examine the stem base to see if it narrows or widens and whether there is an outer case or "volva".*

These diagrams show ways that gills can be attached to the stem.

Gills attached to stem

Gills run down stem

Gills free from stem

Other points to note
Smell Some fungi have a distinct smell that helps to identify them.
Colour of spores Spores are not always the same colour as the gills. To find out what colour they are, make a spore print (see page 58).

How and where it grows Note whether the fungus grows singly, in clusters or in a ring. Note where it grows and which trees are nearby.
When Note the time of year.
Size Measure the width of cap.

*see Glossary, page 60

Cap fungi with pores

The cap fungi on pages 6-9 all have pores underneath the cap. These pores are the openings of a mass of spongy tubes where the spores are produced. The flesh and pores of many species change colour when cut or bruised.

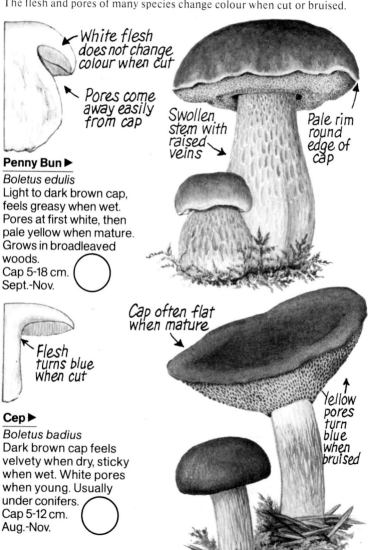

White flesh does not change colour when cut

Pores come away easily from cap

Swollen stem with raised veins

Pale rim round edge of cap

Penny Bun ▶

Boletus edulis
Light to dark brown cap, feels greasy when wet. Pores at first white, then pale yellow when mature. Grows in broadleaved woods.
Cap 5-18 cm.
Sept.-Nov.

Flesh turns blue when cut

Cap often flat when mature

Yellow pores turn blue when bruised

Cep ▶

Boletus badius
Dark brown cap feels velvety when dry, sticky when wet. White pores when young. Usually under conifers.
Cap 5-12 cm.
Aug.-Nov.

6

Cap fungi with pores

Flesh and pores turn blue-green when cut

Red-cracked Boletus ▶

Boletus chrysenteron
When mature, red-brown cap flattens and cracks to show red flesh. Grows in broadleaved woods.
Cap 4-12 cm.
Aug.-Nov.

Yellow flesh and pores

Yellow-cracked Boletus ▶

Boletus subtomentosus
Light to olive brown cap feels velvety and when mature, often cracks to show yellow flesh. Broadleaved woods.
Cap 4-12 cm.
Aug.-Nov.

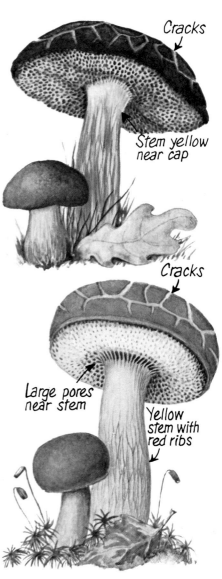

Cracks

Stem yellow near cap

Cracks

Large pores near stem

Yellow stem with red ribs

Cap fungi with pores

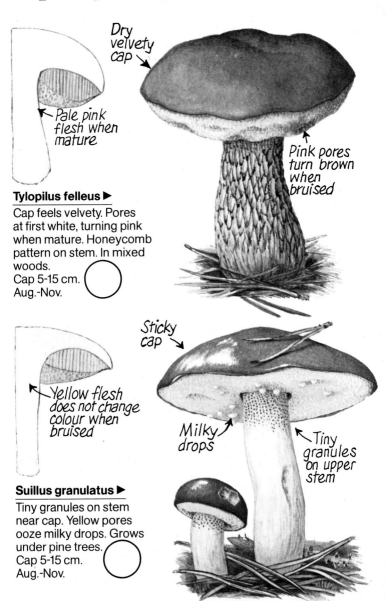

Dry velvety cap →

← Pale pink flesh when mature

Pink pores turn brown when bruised

Tylopilus felleus ▶
Cap feels velvety. Pores at first white, turning pink when mature. Honeycomb pattern on stem. In mixed woods.
Cap 5-15 cm.
Aug.-Nov.

Sticky cap ↘

← Yellow flesh does not change colour when bruised

Milky drops ↗

Tiny granules on upper stem →

Suillus granulatus ▶
Tiny granules on stem near cap. Yellow pores ooze milky drops. Grows under pine trees.
Cap 5-15 cm.
Aug.-Nov.

8

Cap fungi with pores

Dirty white pores darken when bruised

Tall stem with tufts of darker scales

White flesh turns pink when cut

◀ Rough Stemmed
Boletus

Leccinum scabrum
Stem covered with tufts of scales. Pores off-white. Under birch trees.
Cap 6-20 cm.
Aug.-Nov.

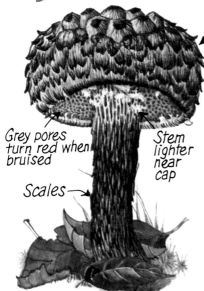

Dark woolly scales on cap

Flesh turns red then black when bruised

Grey pores turn red when bruised

Stem lighter near cap

Scales

◀ Old Man of the Woods

Strobilomyces floccopus
Cap covered with scales, grey at first then brown-black when mature. Dries out without rotting. Broad-leaved woods.
Cap 8-15 cm.
Sept.-Nov.

Cap fungi with gills

The **Amanitas**, pages 10-12, develop from an "egg", enclosed in a white veil, which splits as the stem grows. The remains of the veil at the base of the stem form a "volva". Remains of this veil may also form warts on the cap. Later, a second veil, covering the gills, splits and forms a ring around the stem, although some species do not have a ring. Amanitas have white gills that are free from the stem, and white spores. Several are very poisonous.

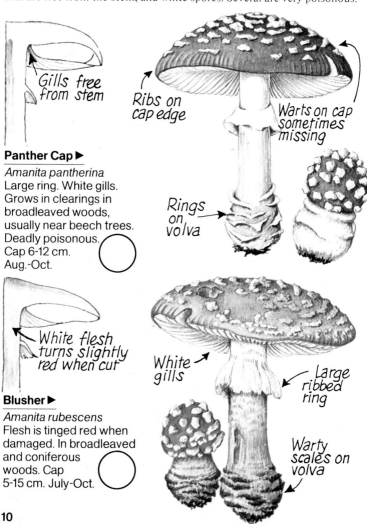

Gills free from stem

Ribs on cap edge

Warts on cap sometimes missing

Rings on volva

Panther Cap ▶

Amanita pantherina
Large ring. White gills. Grows in clearings in broadleaved woods, usually near beech trees. Deadly poisonous. Cap 6-12 cm. Aug.-Oct.

White flesh turns slightly red when cut

White gills

Large ribbed ring

Warty scales on volva

Blusher ▶

Amanita rubescens
Flesh is tinged red when damaged. In broadleaved and coniferous woods. Cap 5-15 cm. July-Oct.

Cap fungi with gills

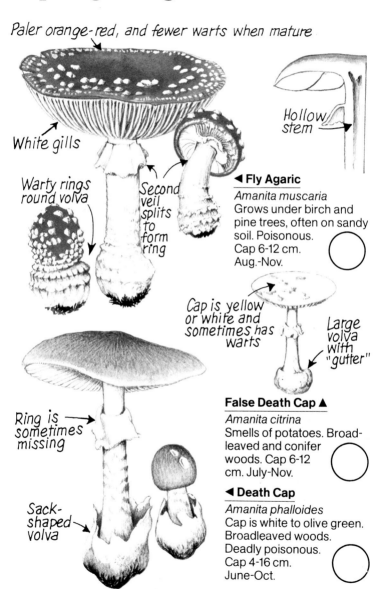

Paler orange-red, and fewer warts when mature

White gills

Warty rings round volva

Second veil splits to form ring

Hollow stem

◀ Fly Agaric

Amanita muscaria
Grows under birch and pine trees, often on sandy soil. Poisonous.
Cap 6-12 cm.
Aug.-Nov.

Cap is yellow or white and sometimes has warts

Large volva with "gutter"

False Death Cap ▲

Amanita citrina
Smells of potatoes. Broad-leaved and conifer woods. Cap 6-12 cm. July-Nov.

Ring is sometimes missing

◀ Death Cap

Amanita phalloides
Cap is white to olive green. Broadleaved woods. Deadly poisonous.
Cap 4-16 cm.
June-Oct.

Sack-shaped volva

Cap fungi with gills

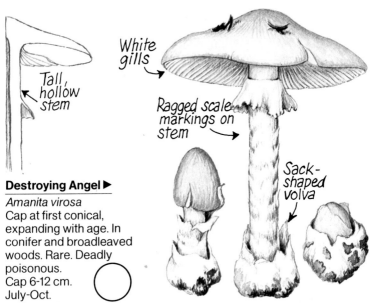

Tall, hollow stem

White gills

Ragged scale markings on stem

Sack-shaped volva

Destroying Angel ▶

Amanita virosa
Cap at first conical,
expanding with age. In
conifer and broadleaved
woods. Rare. Deadly
poisonous.
Cap 6-12 cm.
July-Oct.

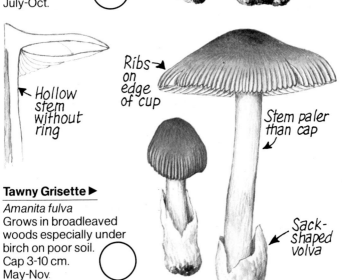

Hollow stem without ring

Ribs on edge of cup

Stem paler than cap

Tawny Grisette ▶

Amanita fulva
Grows in broadleaved
woods especially under
birch on poor soil.
Cap 3-10 cm.
May-Nov.

Sack-shaped volva

Cap fungi with gills

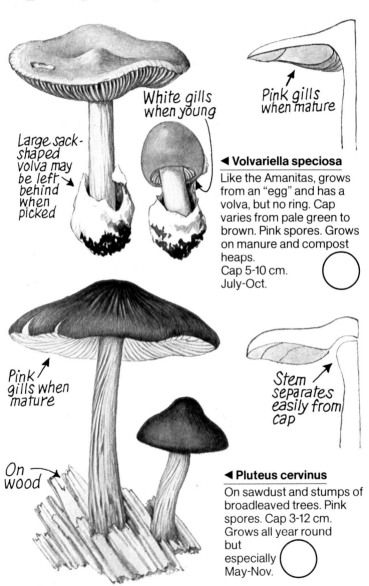

White gills when young

Large sack-shaped volva may be left behind when picked

Pink gills when mature

◄ Volvariella speciosa

Like the Amanitas, grows from an "egg" and has a volva, but no ring. Cap varies from pale green to brown. Pink spores. Grows on manure and compost heaps.
Cap 5-10 cm.
July-Oct.

Pink gills when mature

On wood

Stem separates easily from cap

◄ Pluteus cervinus

On sawdust and stumps of broadleaved trees. Pink spores. Cap 3-12 cm. Grows all year round but especially May-Nov.

Cap fungi with gills

Mushrooms *(Agaricus* group), pages 14-15, develop from a "button" that is covered in a veil that breaks to leave a ring round the stem. The gills are at first pink or grey, but never white, turning dark brown when mature, and are free from the stem. Mushrooms have chocolate-brown spores. Not all are edible.

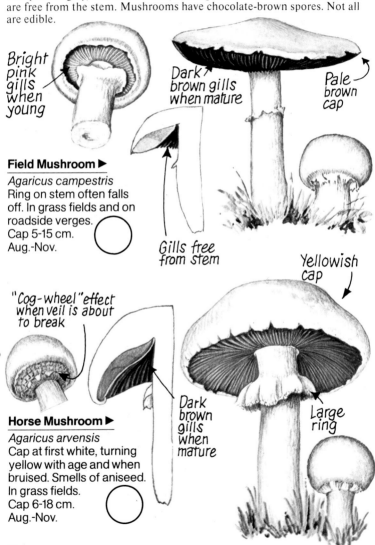

Bright pink gills when young

Dark brown gills when mature

Pale brown cap

Field Mushroom ▶
Agaricus campestris
Ring on stem often falls off. In grass fields and on roadside verges.
Cap 5-15 cm.
Aug.-Nov.

Gills free from stem

Yellowish cap

"Cog-wheel" effect when veil is about to break

Horse Mushroom ▶
Agaricus arvensis
Cap at first white, turning yellow with age and when bruised. Smells of aniseed. In grass fields.
Cap 6-18 cm.
Aug.-Nov.

Dark brown gills when mature

Large ring

14

Cap fungi with gills

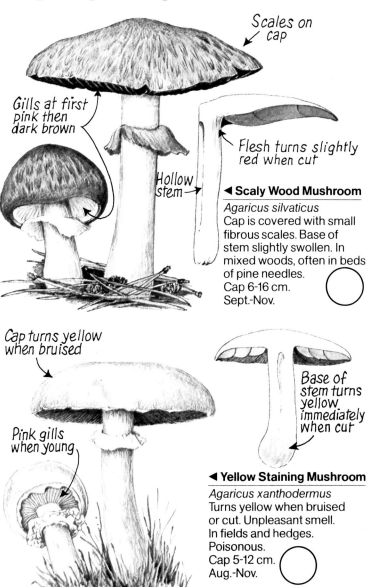

Scales on cap

Gills at first pink then dark brown

Flesh turns slightly red when cut

Hollow stem

◀ **Scaly Wood Mushroom**

Agaricus silvaticus
Cap is covered with small fibrous scales. Base of stem slightly swollen. In mixed woods, often in beds of pine needles.
Cap 6-16 cm.
Sept.-Nov.

Cap turns yellow when bruised

Base of stem turns yellow immediately when cut

Pink gills when young

◀ **Yellow Staining Mushroom**

Agaricus xanthodermus
Turns yellow when bruised or cut. Unpleasant smell. In fields and hedges. Poisonous.
Cap 5-12 cm.
Aug.-Nov.

Cap fungi with gills

Parasols, page 16, have whitish gills, that are free from the stem, and white spores. They have a ring, but no volva, and the stem separates easily from the cap.

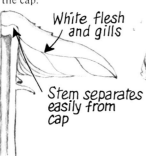

White flesh and gills

Stem separates easily from cap

Scales

Ring

Scaly bands on stem

Cap almost smooth when young

Parasol ▶
Lepiota procera
Stem has snake-like patterns and is swollen at base. In woods and grassy places.
Cap 5-15 cm.
July-Nov.

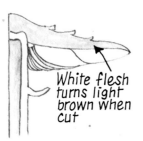

White flesh turns light brown when cut

Scales

Ring

Smooth stem turns red when bruised

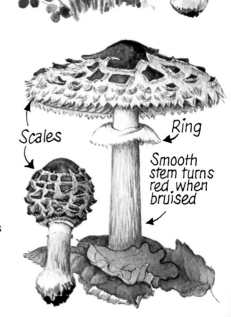

Shaggy Parasol ▶
Lepiota rhacodes
Smooth stem, swollen at base. In clearings in woods and grassy places.
Cap 5-15 cm.
July-Nov.

Cap fungi with gills

Ink Caps, pages 17-18, have thin, crowded gills that often dissolve into a black inky liquid with age. The spores are black.

Cap dissolves with age

Gills white at first, then pink and finally black

White scales

Ring

◄ Shaggy Ink Cap

Coprinus comatus
Slender, hollow stem separates easily from the cap. Often in groups in fields and on roadside verges.
Cap 5-10 cm high.
May-Nov.

White veil covers cap when young →

Cap dissolves with age

◄ Magpie Ink Cap

Coprinus picaceus
Brown-black cap with white patches. Gills at first white, then pale brown, finally black. Broadleaved woods.
Cap 5-10 cm high.
Sept.-Nov.

Cap fungi with gills

Common Ink Cap ▶

Coprinus atramentarius
Gills at first dirty white, turning brown then black. Cap dissolves with age. Usually grows in groups at base of trees, in fields or in woods.
Cap 3-7 cm.
May-Dec.

Ribs on edge of cap

Ring-like zones at base of stem

Ribs on cap

Granules

◀ Glittering Ink Cap

Coprinus micaceus
Tiny granules on cap when young. Gills at first white then black, only dissolving slightly. Grows in groups on tree stumps.
Cap 2-5 cm high.
May-Dec.

Snowy Ink Cap ▶

Coprinus niveus
Gills at first grey, then black. Cap curls and dissolves with age. On cow or horse dung.
Cap 1-3 cm.
May-Nov.

Cap fungi with gills

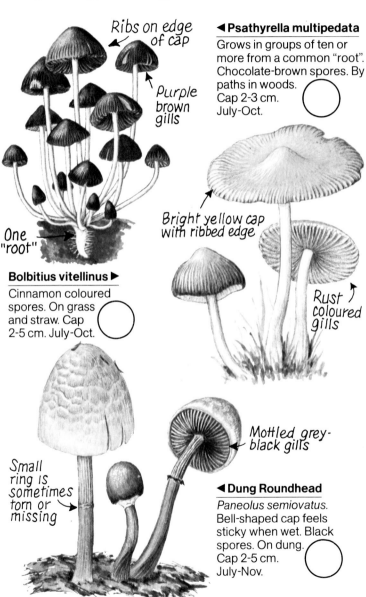

Ribs on edge of cap

Purple brown gills

One "root"

Bolbitius vitellinus ▶
Cinnamon coloured spores. On grass and straw. Cap 2-5 cm. July-Oct.

◀ Psathyrella multipedata
Grows in groups of ten or more from a common "root". Chocolate-brown spores. By paths in woods. Cap 2-3 cm. July-Oct.

Bright yellow cap with ribbed edge

Rust coloured gills

Small ring is sometimes torn or missing

Mottled grey-black gills

◀ Dung Roundhead
Paneolus semiovatus. Bell-shaped cap feels sticky when wet. Black spores. On dung. Cap 2-5 cm. July-Nov.

Cap fungi with gills

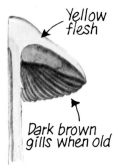

Yellow flesh

Dark brown gills when old

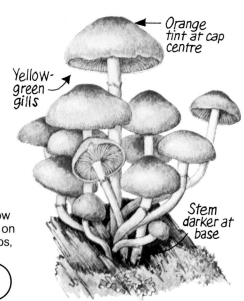

Orange tint at cap centre

Yellow-green gills

Stem darker at base

Sulphur Tuft ▶

Hypholoma fasciculare
Faint ring on stem. Yellow flesh. Grows in clusters on broadleaved tree stumps, often in large numbers. Purple-brown spores. Cap 4-10 cm. Aug.-Nov.

Pale yellow flesh

Dark brown gills when mature

Stem smooth above faint ring

Brick-red Cap ▶

Hypholoma sublaterium
Gills at first yellow, then lilac-grey, finally dark brown. Purple-brown spores. Grows in clusters on tree stumps. Cap 3-8 cm. Sept.-Dec.

Cap fungi with gills

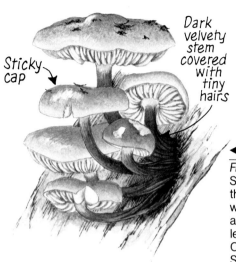

Sticky cap

Dark velvety stem covered with tiny hairs

Pale yellow gills attached to stem

◀ **Velvet Stem**

Flammulina velutipes
Stem ends in a root-like thread. Gills turn brown with age. On trunks, stumps and branches of broad-leaved trees.
Cap 3-8 cm.
Sept.-March.

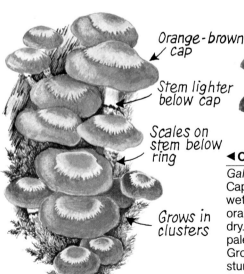

Orange-brown cap

Stem lighter below cap

Scales on stem below ring

Grows in clusters

Cap becomes dark brown when wet

◀ **Cluster Fungus**

Galerina mutabilis
Cap is dark brown when wet, has dark and light orange-brown zones when dry. Thin white gills turn pale brown with age. Grows in clusters on tree stumps.
Cap 4-10 cm.
All year round.

Cap fungi with gills

Brown gills when mature

Scales

Stem smooth above ring

Shaggy Pholiota ▶

Pholiota squarrosa
Yellow gills turn brown with age. Grows in groups at base of broadleaved trees.
Cap 3-8 cm.
Sept.-Nov.

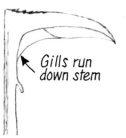

Gills run down stem

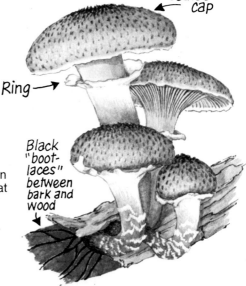

Scales on cap

Ring →

Black "boot-laces" between bark and wood

Honey Fungus ▶

Armillaria mellea
Cream coloured gills turn brown with age. Grows at base of broadleaved or conifer trees which it eventually kills.
Cap 3-10 cm.
July-Dec.

Cap fungi with gills

Wax Caps, page 23, are mainly white or brightly coloured toadstools which look waxy and have well-spaced gills. They have white spores.

Yellow gills when young

Base of stem is white

Widely spaced red gills

◀ Crimson Wax Cap

Hygrophorus puniceus
Cap colour fades with age.
Outline of gills can be seen through the thin cap when it is held up to the light.
In grass fields and roadsides.
Cap 5-12 cm.
Aug.-Dec.

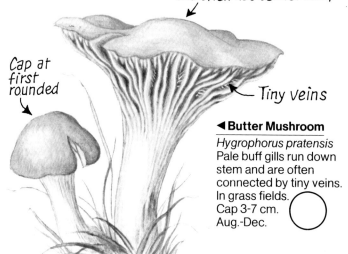

Cap flattens when mature and often has central bump

Cap at first rounded

Tiny veins

◀ Butter Mushroom

Hygrophorus pratensis
Pale buff gills run down stem and are often connected by tiny veins.
In grass fields.
Cap 3-7 cm.
Aug.-Dec.

Cap fungi with gills

Clitocybes, pages 24-25, have whitish or pale gills that run down the stem and the cap is often funnel-shaped. They have white spores.

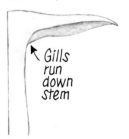

Gills run down stem

Base of stem is swollen and woolly

Aniseed Toadstool ▶

Clitocybe odora
Blue-green cap with central bump. Amongst dead leaves in broad-leaved woods. Smells of aniseed.
Cap 3-7 cm.
Aug.-Nov.

Flesh is thick at centre

Cap darker grey at centre

Edge of cap curves under

Cloudy Cap ▶

Clitocybe nebularis
Grey to grey-brown cap. Grows in woods, especially under pine. Slightly sickly smell.
Cap 6-25 cm.
Aug.-Nov.

Cap fungi with gills

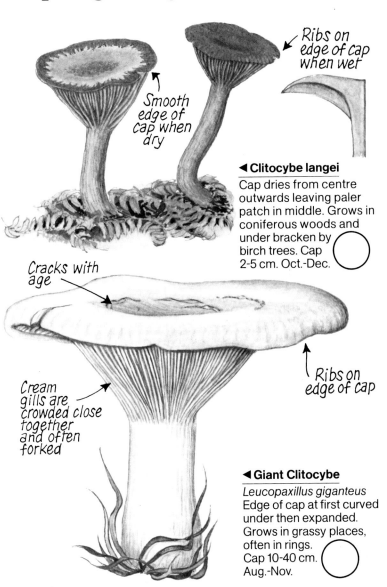

Ribs on edge of cap when wet

Smooth edge of cap when dry

◀ Clitocybe langei
Cap dries from centre outwards leaving paler patch in middle. Grows in coniferous woods and under bracken by birch trees. Cap 2-5 cm. Oct.-Dec.

Cracks with age

Ribs on edge of cap

Cream gills are crowded close together and often forked

◀ Giant Clitocybe
Leucopaxillus giganteus
Edge of cap at first curved under then expanded. Grows in grassy places, often in rings. Cap 10-40 cm. Aug.-Nov.

Cap fungi with gills

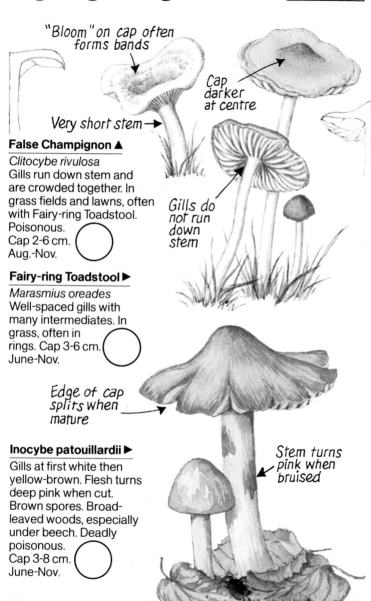

"Bloom" on cap often forms bands

Cap darker at centre

Very short stem →

False Champignon ▲

Clitocybe rivulosa
Gills run down stem and are crowded together. In grass fields and lawns, often with Fairy-ring Toadstool. Poisonous.
Cap 2-6 cm.
Aug.-Nov.

Gills do not run down stem

Fairy-ring Toadstool ▶

Marasmius oreades
Well-spaced gills with many intermediates. In grass, often in rings. Cap 3-6 cm.
June-Nov.

Edge of cap splits when mature

Inocybe patouillardii ▶

Gills at first white then yellow-brown. Flesh turns deep pink when cut. Brown spores. Broad-leaved woods, especially under beech. Deadly poisonous.
Cap 3-8 cm.
June-Nov.

Stem turns pink when bruised

Cap fungi with gills

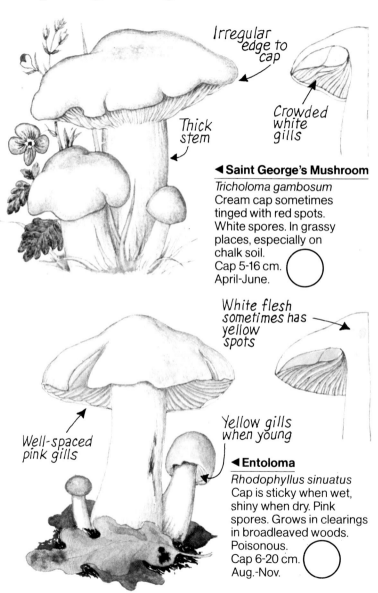

Irregular edge to cap

Crowded white gills

Thick stem

◀ Saint George's Mushroom

Tricholoma gambosum
Cream cap sometimes tinged with red spots. White spores. In grassy places, especially on chalk soil.
Cap 5-16 cm.
April-June.

White flesh sometimes has yellow spots

Well-spaced pink gills

Yellow gills when young

◀ Entoloma

Rhodophyllus sinuatus
Cap is sticky when wet, shiny when dry. Pink spores. Grows in clearings in broadleaved woods. Poisonous.
Cap 6-20 cm.
Aug.-Nov.

Cap fungi with gills

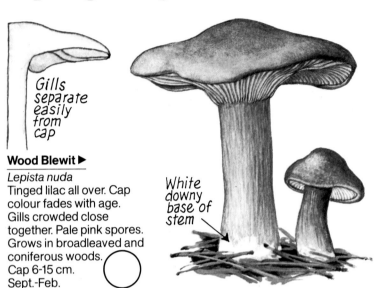

Gills separate easily from cap

Wood Blewit ▶

Lepista nuda
Tinged lilac all over. Cap colour fades with age. Gills crowded close together. Pale pink spores. Grows in broadleaved and coniferous woods.
Cap 6-15 cm.
Sept.-Feb.

White downy base of stem

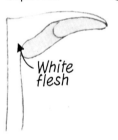

White flesh

Field Blewit ▶

Lepista saeva
Cap varies from pale to dark grey-brown. Cream gills are crowded together. Pale pink spores. In grass fields, wood clearings and hedges.
Cap 5-15 cm.
Sept.-Dec.

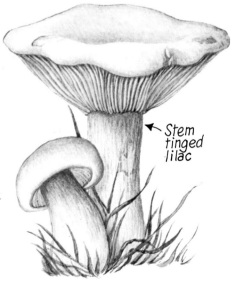

Stem tinged lilac

Cap fungi with gills

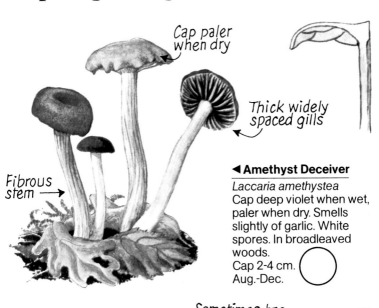

Cap paler when dry

Thick widely spaced gills

Fibrous stem

◀ Amethyst Deceiver

Laccaria amethystea
Cap deep violet when wet, paler when dry. Smells slightly of garlic. White spores. In broadleaved woods.
Cap 2-4 cm.
Aug.-Dec.

Sometimes has fibres on edge of cap

White flesh tinged violet at top of stem

Base of stem is swollen

◀ Lilac Thickfoot

Cortinarius alboviolaceus
Well-spaced gills are violet at first, turning brown when mature. Rust-brown spores. Broadleaved woods, especially beech and oak.
Cap 3-8 cm.
Aug.-Dec.

Cap fungi with gills

Russulas, pages 30-31, have crumbly flesh. The spores and gills are white or cream. Most gills run right from the edge of the cap to the stem, with very few short or "intermediate" gills in between. Many Russulas are brightly coloured. There are almost 100 species in Britain.

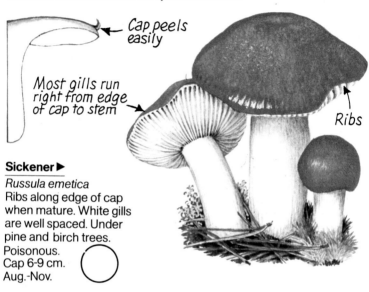

Cap peels easily

Most gills run right from edge of cap to stem

Ribs

Sickener ▶
Russula emetica
Ribs along edge of cap when mature. White gills are well spaced. Under pine and birch trees. Poisonous.
Cap 6-9 cm.
Aug.-Nov.

Gills sometimes have fine rust-coloured spots on edges

Thick stem ▶

Well-spaced cream gills

Russula atropurpurea ▶
Centre of cap is darker colour and often depressed. Broadleaved woods. Cap 5-15 cm. July-Nov.

Cap fungi with gills

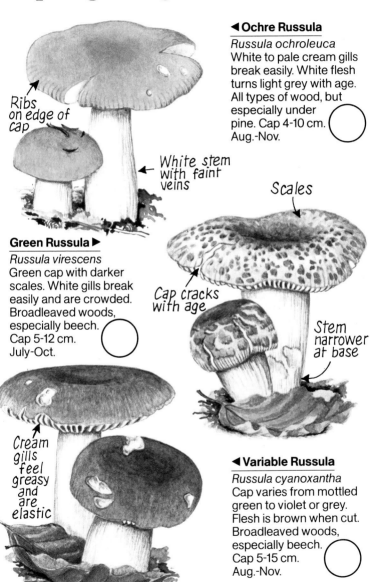

Ribs on edge of cap

White stem with faint veins

◀ Ochre Russula

Russula ochroleuca
White to pale cream gills
break easily. White flesh
turns light grey with age.
All types of wood, but
especially under
pine. Cap 4-10 cm.
Aug.-Nov.

Scales

Cap cracks with age

Stem narrower at base

Green Russula ▶

Russula virescens
Green cap with darker
scales. White gills break
easily and are crowded.
Broadleaved woods,
especially beech.
Cap 5-12 cm.
July-Oct.

Cream gills feel greasy and are elastic

◀ Variable Russula

Russula cyanoxantha
Cap varies from mottled
green to violet or grey.
Flesh is brown when cut.
Broadleaved woods,
especially beech.
Cap 5-15 cm.
Aug.-Nov.

Cap fungi with gills

Milk Caps, pages 32-33, have crumbly flesh and white or pale yellow gills and spores. They ooze white or coloured milky drops when broken.

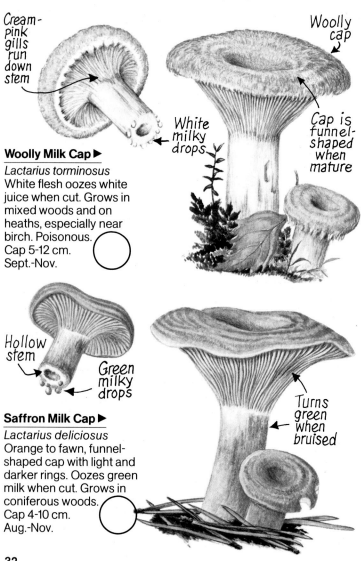

Cream-pink gills run down stem

Woolly cap

White milky drops

Cap is funnel-shaped when mature

Woolly Milk Cap ▶

Lactarius torminosus
White flesh oozes white juice when cut. Grows in mixed woods and on heaths, especially near birch. Poisonous.
Cap 5-12 cm.
Sept.-Nov.

Hollow stem

Green milky drops

Saffron Milk Cap ▶

Lactarius deliciosus
Orange to fawn, funnel-shaped cap with light and darker rings. Oozes green milk when cut. Grows in coniferous woods.
Cap 4-10 cm.
Aug.-Nov.

Turns green when bruised

Cap fungi with gills

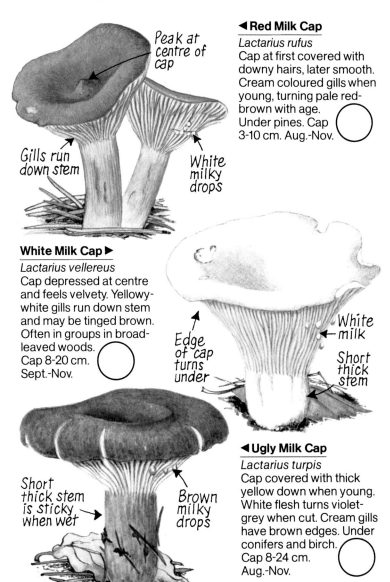

Peak at centre of cap

Gills run down stem

White milky drops

◄ Red Milk Cap

Lactarius rufus
Cap at first covered with downy hairs, later smooth. Cream coloured gills when young, turning pale red-brown with age.
Under pines. Cap 3-10 cm. Aug.-Nov.

White Milk Cap ►

Lactarius vellereus
Cap depressed at centre and feels velvety. Yellowy-white gills run down stem and may be tinged brown. Often in groups in broad-leaved woods.
Cap 8-20 cm.
Sept.-Nov.

Edge of cap turns under

White milk

Short thick stem

Short thick stem is sticky when wet

Brown milky drops

◄ Ugly Milk Cap

Lactarius turpis
Cap covered with thick yellow down when young. White flesh turns violet-grey when cut. Cream gills have brown edges. Under conifers and birch.
Cap 8-24 cm.
Aug.-Nov.

Cap fungi with gills

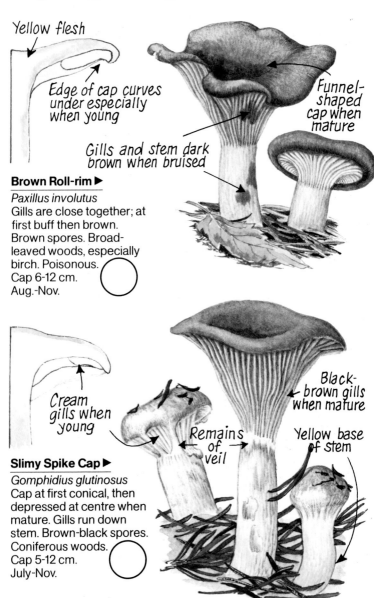

Yellow flesh

Edge of cap curves under especially when young

Funnel-shaped cap when mature

Gills and stem dark brown when bruised

Brown Roll-rim ▶

Paxillus involutus
Gills are close together; at first buff then brown. Brown spores. Broad-leaved woods, especially birch. Poisonous. Cap 6-12 cm. Aug.-Nov.

Cream gills when young

Black-brown gills when mature

Remains of veil

Yellow base of stem

Slimy Spike Cap ▶

Gomphidius glutinosus
Cap at first conical, then depressed at centre when mature. Gills run down stem. Brown-black spores. Coniferous woods. Cap 5-12 cm. July-Nov.

Funnel-shaped fungi

Chanterelle →

False Chanterelle is deeper orange than Chanterelle

True gills run down stem

Thick folds branch near cap

Tiny veins between folds

False Chanterelle ▲
Hygrophoropsis aurantiaca
Thin orange gills. Conifer
woods and heaths.
Poisonous. Cap
4-8 cm. Aug.-Nov.

◄ Chanterelle
Cantharellus cibarius
Fold-like ridges instead of
gills. Smells of apricot.
Broadleaved woods,
especially beech
and oak. Cap
3-10 cm. May-Dec.

Hollow

Dark brown-black when wet

Wrinkles

◄ Horn of Plenty
Craterellus cornucopioides
Funnel-shaped, with
wrinkles on outer surface.
Paler when dry. Broad-
leaved woods.
5-12 cm high.
Aug.-Nov.

Cap fungi with spines

The fungi on this page have a mass of spines, instead of gills or pores, underneath the cap. The spores are produced in these spines.

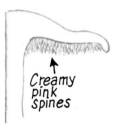

Creamy pink spines

Wood Hedgehog ▶

Hydnum repandum
Cream to light brown cap.
Thick stem is narrower at
base. Often grows in rings
in broadleaved woods,
especially under beech
and oak.
Cap 5-15 cm.
Aug.-Nov.

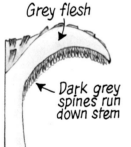

Grey flesh

Dark grey spines run down stem

Sarcodon imbricatum ▶

Grey-brown cap with
darker overlapping scales.
Coniferous woods, usually
on poor sandy soil.
Cap 5-20 cm.
Sept.-Nov.

Bracket fungi with gills

Bracket fungi with gills grow on trees (living wood) or stumps (dead wood). The gills run down a short stem that is usually to one side of the cap.

Cream-violet gills

◀ Little Fan
Schizophyllum commune
Grey, fan-shaped cap.
Tough flesh. Mainly in S.E.
England. On dead branches
and cut timber.
Cap up to 3 cm.
All year round.

Light brown cap with darker rings

Panus torulosus ▶
Tough flesh dries hard.
Flesh-coloured gills run
down stem. Grows on cut
stumps of broadleaved
trees.
Cap 4-14 cm.
May-Oct.

Smooth shell-shaped cap

◀ Oyster Fungus
Pleurotus ostreatus
Cap colour very variable,
may be cream, pale brown,
pale blue, chocolate, or
blue-black. White gills.
Lilac spores. Grows in
groups on broadleaved
trees, sometimes on
coniferous trees.
Cap 5-25 cm.
All year round.

White gills

Bracket fungi with pores

The Bracket fungi with pores, pages 38-40, all grow on trees or stumps and have masses of fine tubes, opening as small pores on the undersurface of the cap. The spores are produced in these tubes.

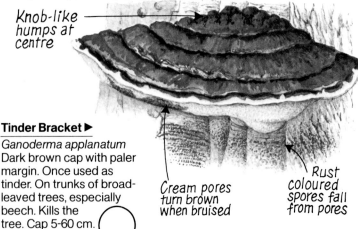

Knob-like humps at centre

Cream pores turn brown when bruised

Rust coloured spores fall from pores

Tinder Bracket ▶

Ganoderma applanatum
Dark brown cap with paler margin. Once used as tinder. On trunks of broad-leaved trees, especially beech. Kills the tree. Cap 5-60 cm. All year round.

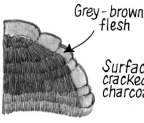

Grey - brown flesh

Surface is cracked like charcoal

Tinder Fungus ▶

Phellinus ignarius
Very hard, grey to black-brown, cracked cap. Tiny pale grey pores turn light brown with age. On broad-leaved trees, especially willow and poplar. Cap 10-30 cm. All year round.

Pale margin

Bracket fungi with pores

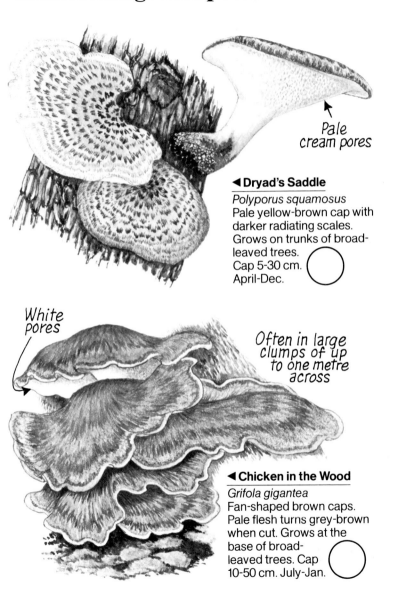

Pale
cream pores

◄ Dryad's Saddle

Polyporus squamosus
Pale yellow-brown cap with
darker radiating scales.
Grows on trunks of broad-
leaved trees.
Cap 5-30 cm.
April-Dec.

White
pores

Often in large
clumps of up
to one metre
across

◄ Chicken in the Wood

Grifola gigantea
Fan-shaped brown caps.
Pale flesh turns grey-brown
when cut. Grows at the
base of broad-
leaved trees. Cap
10-50 cm. July-Jan.

Bracket fungi with pores

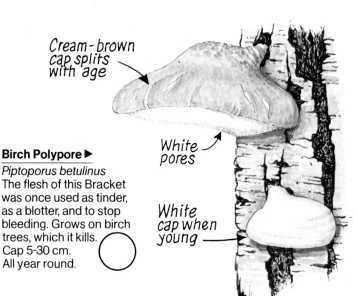

Cream-brown cap splits with age

White pores

White cap when young

Birch Polypore ▶

Piptoporus betulinus
The flesh of this Bracket was once used as tinder, as a blotter, and to stop bleeding. Grows on birch trees, which it kills.
Cap 5-30 cm.
All year round.

Flesh looks like raw meat

Pale red-brown pores

Beef Steak Fungus ▶

Fistulina hepatica
Soft, fleshy fungus that oozes red drops when squeezed. Pores at first yellow then pale red-brown with age. At base of broad-leaved trees, especially oak and chestnut.
Cap 5-30 cm.
Aug.-Nov.

Small brackets and crust fungi

Many fungi form crusts on twigs, trunks, logs or on the ground. Some of these, such as *Trametes serialis*, have pores. Others, like *Stereum hirsutum*, produce spores over their flat or wrinkled undersurface.

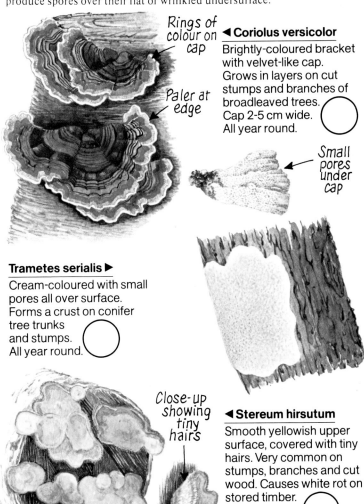

Rings of colour on cap

Paler at edge

◀ Coriolus versicolor

Brightly-coloured bracket with velvet-like cap. Grows in layers on cut stumps and branches of broadleaved trees. Cap 2-5 cm wide. All year round.

Small pores under cap

Trametes serialis ▶

Cream-coloured with small pores all over surface. Forms a crust on conifer tree trunks and stumps. All year round.

Close-up showing tiny hairs

◀ Stereum hirsutum

Smooth yellowish upper surface, covered with tiny hairs. Very common on stumps, branches and cut wood. Causes white rot on stored timber. 1-4 cm across. All year round.

Stinkhorn, Saddle Cap

 Cross-section of "egg"

 Spores

Stinkhorn ▶

Phallus impudicus
Develops from a white
"egg", buried in leaves or
moss. Dark slime on head
of stem contains spores
and is soon eaten by flies.
Very strong, unpleasant
smell. Grows in woods and
hedgerows.
6-12 cm high.
July-Oct.

 "Egg"

 Deep grooves on stem

Saddle Cap ▶

Helvella crispa
Hollow stem is capped by
folds that are off-white on
the upper side and pale
fawn underneath. Beside
paths in broadleaved
woods. 5-10 cm
high. March, April
and Aug.-Oct.

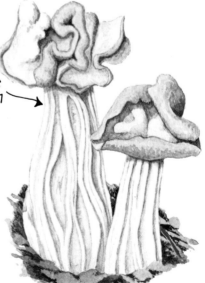

Morel, Turban Fungus

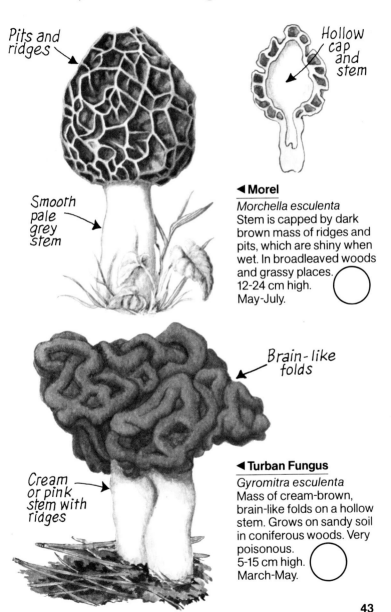

Pits and ridges

Hollow cap and stem

Smooth pale grey stem

◄ Morel
Morchella esculenta
Stem is capped by dark brown mass of ridges and pits, which are shiny when wet. In broadleaved woods and grassy places.
12-24 cm high.
May-July.

Brain-like folds

Cream or pink stem with ridges

◄ Turban Fungus
Gyromitra esculenta
Mass of cream-brown, brain-like folds on a hollow stem. Grows on sandy soil in coniferous woods. Very poisonous.
5-15 cm high.
March-May.

Cup fungi

Cup fungi grow on logs, tree trunks or on the ground. Their spores are produced from the inside of the cup.

Scarlet Elf Cup ▶

Sarcoscypha coccinea
Smooth, scarlet surface inside cup; downy, cream or orange outer surface. On rotting branches of broadleaved trees. Cup 2-5 cm wide. Dec.-March.

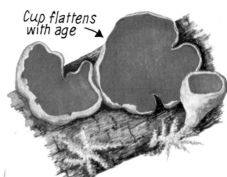

Cup flattens with age

◀ Peziza badia

Outside surface of cup is paler brown than inside. On the ground, in broad-leaved woods. Poisonous. Cup 3-7 cm wide. Aug.-Oct.

Edge of cup often splits with age

Orange Peel Fungus ▶

Aleuria aurantia
Smooth, orange surface inside cup; downy, paler orange outer surface. On gravel, lawns and on bare soil in woods. Cup 1-12 cm wide. Aug.-Dec.

Cup fungus, Bird's Nest Fungus, Truffle

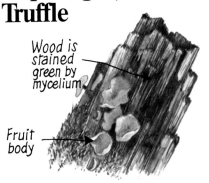

Wood is stained green by mycelium

Fruit body

Chlorosplenium aeruginascens
Tiny, green cup-shaped fruit bodies. Wood on which it grows is permanently stained green. Grows on rotting wood, especially oak. Cup 0.5 cm wide. May-Nov.

Bird's Nest Fungus ▶

Crucibulum vulgare
Small cup-shaped fungus, filled with several egg-shaped bodies which contain spores. Rain splashes the "eggs" out of the cup and the spores can then disperse. On twigs. Cup 0.5-1 cm high. Sept.-Feb.

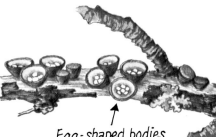

Egg-shaped bodies contain spores

Marbled flesh

Rough warty surface

◀ Cook's Truffle

Tuber aestivum
This is one of several kinds of truffles. Grey flesh, sometimes tinged lilac, streaked with paler veins. Grows in soil, just below ground level, in beech woods, especially in chalk soil. 3-8 cm across. Aug.-Oct.

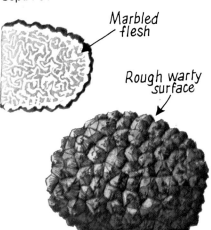

45

Puffballs

Puffballs are round or pear-shaped fungi with a skin that is either smooth
or covered with small warts. Their spores are produced inside the "ball"
and, when ripe, are dispersed either through a small hole that forms in the
top of the ball, or through cracks over the surface.

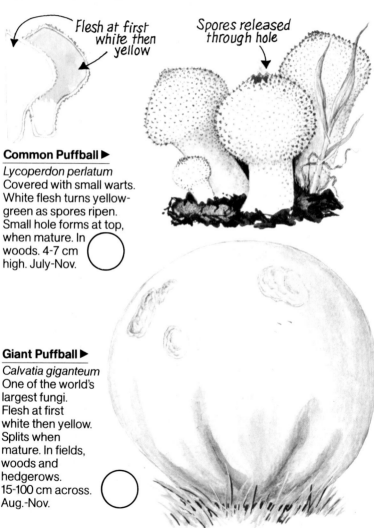

Flesh at first white then yellow

Spores released through hole

Common Puffball ▶

Lycoperdon perlatum
Covered with small warts.
White flesh turns yellow-
green as spores ripen.
Small hole forms at top,
when mature. In
woods. 4-7 cm
high. July-Nov.

Giant Puffball ▶

Calvatia giganteum
One of the world's
largest fungi.
Flesh at first
white then yellow.
Splits when
mature. In fields,
woods and
hedgerows.
15-100 cm across.
Aug.-Nov.

Puffball, Earthball, Earth Star

◀ Puffball
Calvatia caelatum
Grey-brown at first, turning dark brown with age. Top opens out to release dark brown spores. In fields and woods on sandy soil. 6-10 cm across. July-Nov.

Black centre when mature

Common Earthball ▶
Scleroderma aurantium
Looks like a young puffball, but is much harder and no hole forms. Centre is at first cream, then yellow and finally black. In woods, especially under birch.
4-8 cm across.
July-Dec.

Hard warty surface

Onion-shaped at first

Note:
There are other kinds of earthballs and earthstars

"Collar" round centre

◀ Earth Star
Geastrum triplex
Onion-shaped at first, then outer layer peels back forming 5-7 pointed arms. Broadleaved woods, especially beech.
6-8 cm across.
Aug.-Nov.

Jelly fungi

Many fungi have a jelly-like texture, especially when wet. Some jelly fungi are irregular in shape and grow in clusters.

Witch's Butter ▶

Exidia glandulosa
Deep olive to black coloured jelly. Grows in mass of varying size on rotting stumps of broad-leaved trees. All year round, but mainly Oct.-Dec.

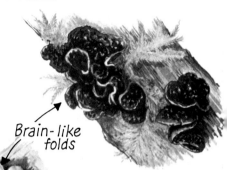

Brain-like folds

◀ Yellow Brain Fungus

Tremella mesenterica
Slimy when wet, drying to a hard, orange crust. Grows in mass of varying size on dead branches and tree stumps. All year round, but mainly Sept.-Dec.

Soft and velvety when wet

Dries to a hard crust

Ear Fungus ▶

Auricularia auricula
Mainly on branches of elder trees. Each ear 3-10 cm across. All year round.

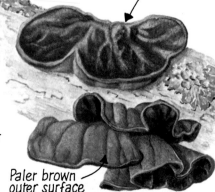

Paler brown outer surface

Cauliflower Fungus, Fairy Clubs

Fairy Clubs may be branched, like the Coral Fungus, or unbranched, like the Giant Club. They have a leathery texture and, like some of the jelly fungi, produce their spores all over their surface.

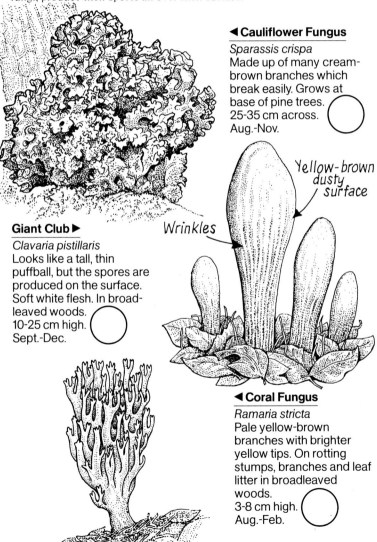

◄ Cauliflower Fungus

Sparassis crispa
Made up of many cream-brown branches which break easily. Grows at base of pine trees.
25-35 cm across.
Aug.-Nov.

Yellow-brown dusty surface

Wrinkles

Giant Club ►

Clavaria pistillaris
Looks like a tall, thin puffball, but the spores are produced on the surface. Soft white flesh. In broad-leaved woods.
10-25 cm high.
Sept.-Dec.

◄ Coral Fungus

Ramaria stricta
Pale yellow-brown branches with brighter yellow tips. On rotting stumps, branches and leaf litter in broadleaved woods.
3-8 cm high.
Aug.-Feb.

"Soot" fungi

In this group, the spores are produced over the surface of the fungus from tiny flask-shaped bodies buried in the surface.

Cramp Balls ▶

Daldinia concentrica
Hard, brown or black, ball-shaped fungus with shiny surface. Has dark and pale circular zones inside. Grows on dead trees, especially ash.
2-8 cm across.
All year round.

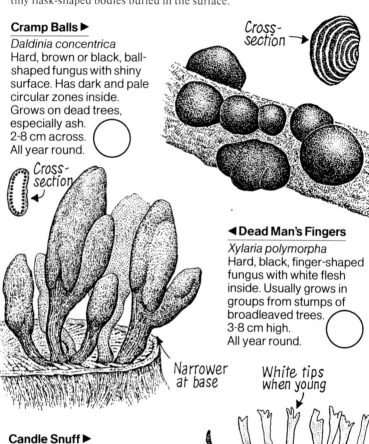

Cross-section

◀ Dead Man's Fingers

Xylaria polymorpha
Hard, black, finger-shaped fungus with white flesh inside. Usually grows in groups from stumps of broadleaved trees.
3-8 cm high.
All year round.

Cross-section

Narrower at base

White tips when young

Candle Snuff ▶

Xylaria hypoxylon
Black stem with white tip which turns black with age. On dead wood and tree stumps.
2-6 cm high.
All year round.

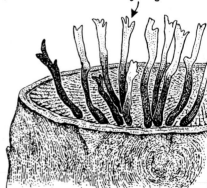

How fungi live

Most plants contain chlorophyll, a green substance that enables them to make their own food. Fungi do not contain chlorophyll and so have to feed on plant or animal matter. Some fungi feed only on dead matter. Others feed on living plants or animals, which they may harm or benefit.

Saprophytes
Fungi that feed on dead plants or animals are called saprophytes. *Coriolus versicolor,* shown growing on a dead tree stump in the picture, is an example of this type of fungus. Saprophytes are usually useful as they help to break down dead matter.

Parasites
Fungi that feed on living plants or animals are called parasites. Many parasites damage, and some may even kill, the plant or animal they live on. Birch Polypore eventually kills the birch tree it grows on.

Symbiotic fungi
Symbiotic fungi grow on living plants, but do not damage them. The fungus and plant help each other. Fly Agaric grows symbiotically with birch or pine trees and its mycelium grows around the tree roots. The tree provides the fungus with sugars that it needs and the fungus passes on to the tree nutrients that it has broken down from dead leaves. This process allows birch trees to survive in poor soil.

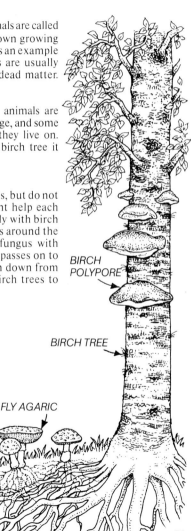

BIRCH POLYPORE

BIRCH TREE

CORIOLUS VERSICOLOR

FLY AGARIC

Useful fungi

Fungi, together with bacteria, are essential to life on earth. They break down the bodies of dead plants and animals. As they do this, they return to the soil the nutrients that the plant or animal absorbed when it was alive.

Besides the fungi shown in this book, there are thousands of small fungi, many of which are too small to be seen with the human eye. Several of these small fungi are used to make food, drink and medicines.

Yeast

Yeast cells magnified

Yeast grows on grape skins

Wine

Beer

Bread

Yeast has been used for thousands of years to make alcohol and bread. It is a microscopic saprophytic fungus that lives on sugars. It grows naturally on the skin of fruit, but today it is grown industrially for making food and drink.

The alcohol in wine and beer is produced when yeast breaks down the sugar in fruit juice. Yeast also produces gas which forms the bubbles in beer, champagne and cider.

Yeast is the substance that makes bread rise. When it is added to bread dough it breaks down the sugar and releases gas that makes the bread rise.

Penicillium moulds

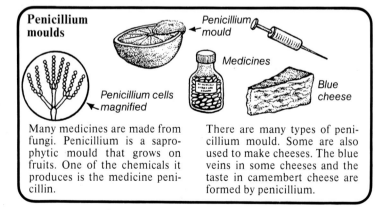

Penicillium mould

Medicines

Penicillium cells magnified

Blue cheese

Many medicines are made from fungi. Penicillium is a saprophytic mould that grows on fruits. One of the chemicals it produces is the medicine penicillin.

There are many types of penicillium mould. Some are also used to make cheeses. The blue veins in some cheeses and the taste in camembert cheese are formed by penicillium.

Harmful fungi

Some of the fungi that live off dead matter cause damage to our food stores and buildings. Most harm is done by parasitic fungi that grow on living plants and animals. They can destroy crops and plants.

Dry Rot

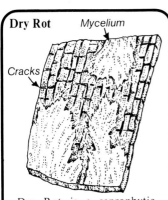

Mycelium

Cracks

Dry Rot is a saprophytic fungus that lives on timber inside buildings. It makes the wood crack and eventually crumble away. Dry Rot does not attack wood outside as it cannot survive changes in humidity.

Dutch Elm disease

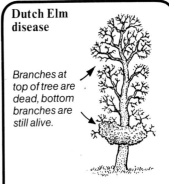

Branches at top of tree are dead, bottom branches are still alive.

Dutch Elm disease is caused by a parasitic fungus that blocks the circulation of water around the tree. The branches at the top of the tree die first. The fungus is carried from tree to tree by the Elm Bark Beetle.

Rose Mildew

Blotches

There are many types of parasitic mildew that attack plants. Rose mildew is a fungus that grows inside the leaves of rose bushes. Blotches appear on the leaves and the whole plant becomes unhealthy.

Athlete's Foot

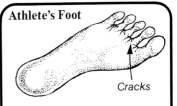

Cracks

Some fungi live on the skin of animals and humans. Athlete's Foot is caused by a parasitic fungus that lives on the skin of the sole of people's feet. The skin becomes hard and cracks between the toes.

How a mushroom grows

Both the mycelium, which lives buried in the soil, and the mushroom (or fruit body) which appears above ground, are made up of tiny thread-like tubes called "hyphae". The mycelium is made up of loosely arranged hyphae and the mushroom is made up of tightly packed hyphae. Hyphae develop from spores that are produced in the gills of a mushroom. The pictures below show how a mushroom develops.

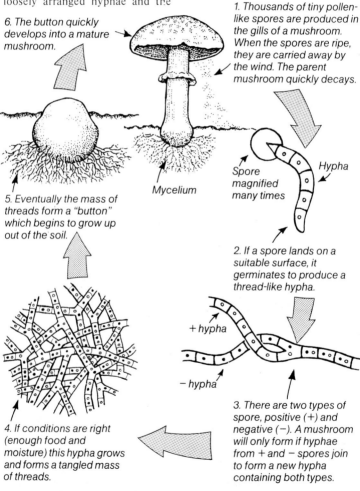

6. The button quickly develops into a mature mushroom.

Mycelium

5. Eventually the mass of threads form a "button" which begins to grow up out of the soil.

1. Thousands of tiny pollen-like spores are produced in the gills of a mushroom. When the spores are ripe, they are carried away by the wind. The parent mushroom quickly decays.

Spore magnified many times

Hypha

2. If a spore lands on a suitable surface, it germinates to produce a thread-like hypha.

+ hypha

− hypha

4. If conditions are right (enough food and moisture) this hypha grows and forms a tangled mass of threads.

3. There are two types of spore, positive (+) and negative (−). A mushroom will only form if hyphae from + and − spores join to form a new hypha containing both types.

Fairy rings

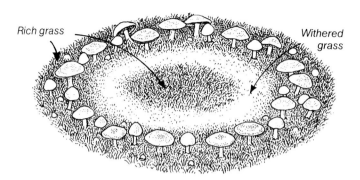

Rich grass

Withered grass

Some fungi, such as the Fairy Ring Toadstool, are found in rings. These rings are marked not only by toadstools which appear in autumn, but also sometimes by outer and inner rings of dark, lush grass. The rings of rich grass may be separated by an area of withered grass.

Fairy rings grow outwards at a rate of 15-35 centimetres a year. Some rings grow very large and may be hundreds of years old. The pictures below show how a fairy ring develops.

1

Mycelium

Mycelium spreads outwards in search of organic matter in the soil to feed on.

2

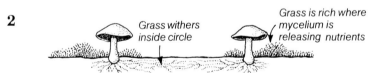

Grass withers inside circle

Grass is rich where mycelium is releasing nutrients

Dark, rich grass grows at the edge of the mycelium as it creeps outwards. This happens as nutrients are released as the mycelium begins to break down organic matter. These nutrients feed the grass as well as the fungi. Inside the circle, where the mycelium has absorbed most of the goodness from the soil, the grass may wither.

3

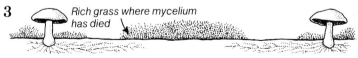

Rich grass where mycelium has died

Year by year, the fungus mycelium spreads outwards. Eventually an inner zone of rich grass may form. This is where the old mycelium has died, releasing its nutrients into the soil for the grass to absorb.

Spotting and collecting fungi

Where to look

Each type of fungus grows in a particular place or habitat. Some grow only in broadleaved woods, such as beechwoods, others grow only in coniferous woods under trees such as pine. Some fungi grow in open grassland. Wherever there are trees, dead wood or grass and moist conditions there are usually some fungi to be found.

In each habitat there will be different fungi growing on the ground, on tree trunks, on dead wood and in leaf litter. Look carefully in all of these places.

What to take with you

When you go out to spot fungi, take this book and a notebook and pencil so that you can record your finds. Take a tape measure to measure fungi, and a magnifying glass to help you take a closer look at gills, pores and stems. Draw the fungi you find and note down details about them. Be sure to include a note about where each one grows and try to identify any trees nearby. If you find a fungus that is not in this book, your notes and drawing will help you to identify it from other books later.

Collecting fungi

You may want to take some fungi home with you to examine them more closely. If you do this, never take more than one of each kind and do not pick a fungus if you know it is rare. When you pick a mushroom or toadstool, be sure to get the whole of the stem so that you can tell if it has a volva.

You will need an open basket to carry the fungi in. A small box, like a large match box, is useful for carrying small, fragile toadstools. Never put fungi in plastic bags as they will quickly start to rot.

Remember never to eat or taste any fungus unless an expert has assured you that it is absolutely safe.

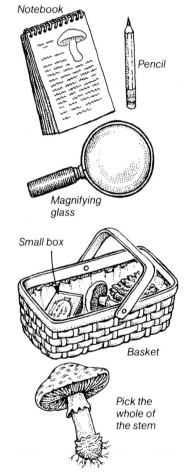

Notebook

Pencil

Magnifying glass

Small box

Basket

Pick the whole of the stem

Preserving fungi

Bracket fungi

Most kinds of fungi can only be kept for a short time before they begin to rot. Some of the tough, woody bracket fungi, like Tinder Bracket, can be dried without losing their colour or shape and make good ornaments. To dry a bracket fungus, just leave it for a few days in a warm, dry place, such as near a radiator.

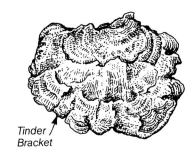

Tinder Bracket

Mushrooms and toadstools

Most mushrooms and toadstools cannot be dried without losing their shape and colour. But you can preserve a record of the shape of a mushroom and the way its gills are attached to the stem by drying a slice of it.

To do this, cut a thin section through the centre of the fungus and place it between two pieces of blotting paper. Place a heavy book on top of the blotting paper and leave it for a day or two until the slice is quite dry. If you make a drawing of the toadstool, you can then glue the dried slice on to the same piece of paper beside your drawing.

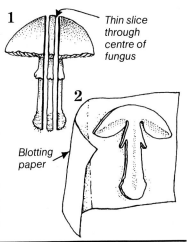

1 Thin slice through centre of fungus

2

Blotting paper

Drawing fungi

The best way to keep a record of fungi you find is to make a coloured drawing. Write notes beside the drawing describing the fungus (see page 5) and be sure to note where and when it was found. This will help you to remember the fungus and to recognize it easily the next time you spot it.

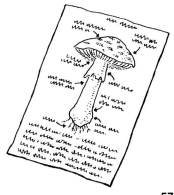

How to make a spore print

To make a spore print you will need a mature, undamaged cap. Good spore prints can be taken only from fungi with gills. It is difficult to make one from fungi that have pores.

First cut off the stalk close to the cap.

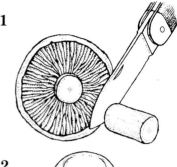

Place the cap on a piece of paper, with the gills facing down. If the gills are dark, use white paper, if they are white, use black paper. Cover the cap with a jar or bowl to protect it from draughts and leave it overnight.

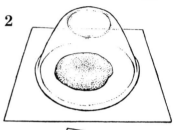

When you lift up the cap, a print will be left by the spores that have fallen from the gills. You can preserve the print by spraying it lightly with a varnish spray or fixative, which you can buy from an artist's supplies shop. When the spray is dry, test the edge of the print with a paint brush. If spores come away, add more varnish until there is no more smudging.

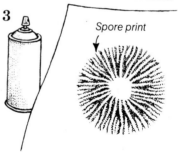

Spore print

Looking at spores

If you have the opportunity to use a microscope, try looking at some spores through it. You can collect these by making a spore print. Examine the spores of different kinds of fungi. Each type of fungus has spores of a particular shape. The colour, size and shape of spores are very important to experts for identification of fungi.

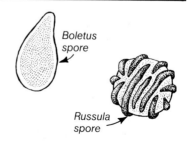

Boletus spore

Russula spore

How to make a fungus garden

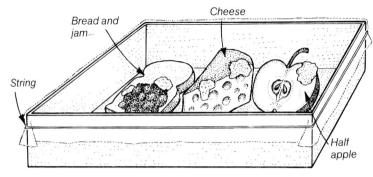

Cheese

Bread and jam

String

Half apple

Most of the fungi shown in this book grow on outdoor substances, such as wood or dead leaves, and cannot be grown at home. Their mycelium often has to grow for several years before mushrooms or toadstools are formed. It is possible however, to grow other types of small fungi, especially moulds.

To make a fungus garden, find a shallow box or tin. Put in it half an apple, a piece of cheese and a slice of damp bread half spread with jam. You can also experiment with other types of food.

Cover the box or tin tightly with clear plastic film or put the whole box into a sealed, clear plastic bag. Leave it in a warm place for a week or two.

Every few days inspect the box and see what has grown on the pieces of food. Do not take the plastic cover off, but look through it and make notes about the shapes and colour of the fungus growths. If you have a magnifying glass, you can examine the moulds more closely.

When you have finished studying the fungi, put the whole box into the dustbin, without taking the cover off.

Growing spores

Although it is difficult to grow large fungi, you can watch how mycelium begins to form. To do this, melt some gelatine in hot water and mix it up with some dead leaves, cut in small pieces. When the mixture has cooled, sprinkle a few spores onto it. You can get spores by making a spore print. Keep the jelly mixture covered and examine it every day with a strong magnifying glass.

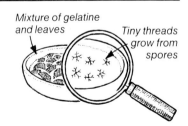

Mixture of gelatine and leaves

Tiny threads grow from spores

After a few days you may see tiny threads just creeping from the spores over the surface of the jelly.

Glossary

Broadleaved tree – A tree with broad flat leaves. Most broadleaved trees, such as beech and oak, shed their leaves in autumn.

Coniferous tree – Most conifers have needle-like leaves that are shed all the year round.

Fruit body – The part of a fungus that produces spores. It is the part that most people recognize as a fungus. It usually appears above ground only at certain times of the year.

Gills – The ribs on the underside of a mushroom which radiate out from the stem like spokes of a wheel.

Habitat – The place where a fungus grows, for example grassland.

Hyphae – The tiny threads that make up fungus mycelium and fruit bodies.

Intermediate gill – A gill that does not run all the way from the edge of the cap to the stem.

Mixed wood – A wood which has both broadleaved and coniferous trees.

Mycelium – The mass of hyphae of which a fungus is made and from which fruit bodies form. It lives buried in the plant or animal matter it feeds on.

Mycology – The study of fungi.

Mushroom – Cap fungus with gills that belongs to the *Agaricus* group (see page 14). Some people call all edible cap fungi "mushrooms".

Nutrients – The goodness in soil on which fungi feed.

Pores – The round openings of tubes, on the underside of the cap of the *Boletus* group and most bracket fungi.

Ring – The remains of the veil left on the stem of a cap fungus.

Spores – The "seeds" of a fungus. They are tiny dust-like particles produced in the gills or tubes of cap fungi.

Spines – Small teeth-like projections instead of gills, under the cap of some fungi (see page 36).

Toadstool – A general term for any cap fungus with a stem.

Veil – The outer "skin" of a young toadstool that splits to reveal the gills.

Volva – The remains of the veil at the base of the stem. All Amanitas have a volva (see page 10).

Clubs to join

Many local **natural history societies** organize fungus forays in autumn and young members are always welcome. You can find out the address of your nearest natural history society from your local library.

The British Mycological Society is an organisation for people interested in fungi. The society organizes forays led by experts throughout the country. Young people can join as associate members and will be sent details of forays organized by the society and by local natural history societies in all parts of the country. Write to Dr. N. J. Dix (BMS Membership Secretary) Department of Biology, University of Stirling, Scotland FK9 4LA, or to Dr. R. J. Bevan, Department of Biology, N. E. Surrey College of Technology, Ewell, Surrey.

Books to read

Here are some more guide books which will help you identify any fungi you find that are not shown in this book. You might be able to borrow them from your local library.

Collins Guide to Mushrooms and Toadstools. Lange & Hora (Collins).
Mushrooms and Toadstools. G. Kibby (OUP).
Fungi of Northern Europe Books 1 & 2. Nilsson & Persson (Penguin Nature Guides).
The Encyclopedia of Mushrooms. Dickinson & Lucas (Orbis).

Mushrooms and Other Fungi. Rinaldi & Tyndalo (Hamlyn).
Identification of the Larger Fungi. R. Watling (Hutton).

If you want to learn more about the biology of fungi, the following books provide a good introduction.

Beginner's Guide to the Fungi. C. L. Duddington (Pelham Books).
Wayside and Woodland Fungi. Findlay (Warne).
Mushrooms and Toadstools. J. Ramsbottom (Collins New Naturalist Series).

Scorecard

The fungi in this scorecard are arranged in alphabetical order. When you spot a fungus, fill in the date next to its name. You can add up your score after a day out spotting.

	Score	Date seen		Score	Date seen
Amethyst Deceiver	10		Blusher	10	
Aniseed Toadstool	10		Bolbitius vitellinus	15	
Beef Steak Fungus	15		Boletus, Red-cracked	10	
Birch Polypore	5		Boletus, Rough Stemmed	15	
Bird's Nest Fungus	10		Boletus, Yellow-cracked	10	
Blewit, Field	15		Brick-red Cap	15	
Blewit, Wood	15		Brown Roll Rim	10	
Blue Stain Fungus	20		Candle Snuff	15	

	Score	Date seen		Score	Date seen
Cauliflower Fungus	15		Giant Club	20	
Cep	10		Honey Fungus	10	
Chanterelle	15		Horn of Plenty	15	
Chanterelle, False	10		Ink Cap, Common	10	
Chicken in the Wood	15		Ink Cap, Glittering	10	
Clitocybe, Giant	20		Ink Cap, Magpie	15	
Clitocybe langei	10		Ink Cap, Shaggy	5	
Cloudy Cap	15		Ink Cap, Snowy	15	
Cluster Fungus	15		Inocybe patouillardii	15	
Coral Fungus	15		Lilac Thickfoot	15	
Coriolus versicolor	5		Little Fan	15	
Cramp Balls	10		Milk Cap, Red	10	
Dead Man's Finger	15		Milk Cap, Saffron	15	
Death Cap	15		Milk Cap, Ugly	15	
Destroying Angel	25		Milk Cap, White	15	
Dryad's Saddle	10		Milk Cap, Woolly	10	
Dung Roundhead	10		Morel	25	
Ear Fungus	5		Mushroom, Butter	15	
Earthball, Common	10		Mushroom, Field	10	
Earth Star	20		Mushroom, Horse	10	
Entoloma	15		Mushroom, Saint George's	15	
Fairy Ring Toadstool	10		Mushroom, Scaly Wood	15	
False Champignon	10		Mushroom, Yellow Staining	15	
False Death Cap	15		Old Man of the Woods	15	
Fly Agaric	15		Orange Peel Fungus	15	

	Score	Date seen		Score	Date seen
Oyster Fungus	15		Sickener	10	
Panther Cap	5		Slimy Spike Cap	15	
Panus torulosus	10		Stereum hirsutum	5	
Parasol	10		Stinkhorn	15	
Parasol, Shaggy	10		Suillus granulatus	15	
Penny Bun	15		Sulphur Tuft	10	
Peziza badia	20		Tawny Grisette	10	
Pluteus cervinus	15		Tinder Bracket	10	
Psathyrella multipedata	20		Tinder Fungus	20	
Puffball	15		Trametes serialis	15	
Puffball, Common	15		Truffle, Cook's	25	
Puffball, Giant	20		Turban Fungus	20	
Russula atropurpurea	10		Tylopilus felleus	15	
Russula, Ochre	15		Velvet Stem	10	
Russula, Variable	15		Volvariella speciosa	15	
Russula virescens	15		Wax Cap, Crimson	20	
Saddle Cap	20		Witch's Butter	15	
Sarcodon imbricatum	15		Wood Hedgehog	15	
Scarlet Elf Cup	15		Yellow Brain Fungus	10	
Shaggy Pholiota	15				

Index

All scientific names are written in italics.